He's sad.

Il est triste.

"Would you like an orange?"
says Python.

"Est-ce que tu veux une orange?"
dit le Python.

I want my banana!

Je veux ma banane!

Mary Risk

Pictures by Alex de Wolf
French by Jacqueline Jansen

b small publishing

Monkey has lost his banana.

Le Singe a perdu sa banane.

"It's nice and juicy."

"C'est bon et juteux."

"No, thanks," says Monkey.

"Non, merci," dit le Singe.

"I want my banana."

"Je veux ma banane."

"Have some nuts," says Parrot.

"Prends quelques noix," dit le Perroquet.

"They're delicious."

"Elles sont délicieuses."

"No, thanks," says Monkey.

"Non, merci," dit le Singe.

"I only like bananas."

"Je n'aime que les bananes."

"Have a pineapple," says Hyena.

"Prends un ananas," dit la Hyène.

"It's very sweet."

"C'est très sucré."

"No, thanks," says Monkey.

"Non, merci," dit le Singe.

"I just want my banana."

"Je veux seulement ma banane."

"Come here, little Monkey,"
says Tiger.

"Viens par ici, petit Singe,"
dit le Tigre.

"I'll give you your banana."

"Je vais te la donner, ta banane."

But Monkey sees his banana.

Mais le Singe voit sa banane.

And he gets it just in time!

Et il l'attrape juste à temps!

Monkey's happy now.

Le Singe est heureux maintenant.

"Bananas are best," he says.

"Les bananes, c'est ce qu'il y a de mieux," dit-il.

Pronouncing French

Don't worry if your pronunciation isn't quite correct. The important thing is to be willing to try.

The pronunciation guide here will help but it cannot be completely accurate:

- Read the guide as naturally as possible, as if it were British English.
- Put stress on the letters in *italics* e.g. lombool-*onss*.
- Don't roll the r at the end of the word, for example in the French word **le** (the): ler.

If you can, ask a French person to help and move on as soon as possible to speaking the words without the guide.

Note French adjectives usually have two forms, one for masculine and one for feminine nouns. They often look very similar but are pronounced slightly differently e.g **juteux** and **juteuse** (see below).

Words Les mots

leh moh

monkey

le singe

ler sanjsh

python

le python

ler pee*toh*

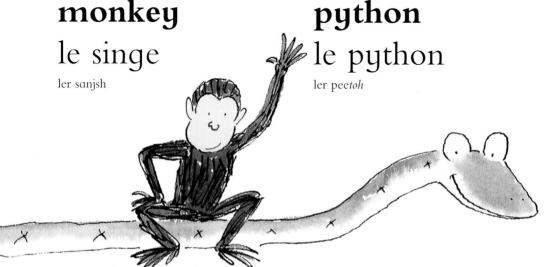

parrot
le perroquet
ler pair-o-*keh*

hyena
la hyène
lah ee*yen*

tiger
le tigre
ler teegr'

banana
la banane
lah ban-*nahn*

orange
l'orange
loh-*ronjsh*

nuts
les noix
leh nwah

pineapple
l'ananas
lan-an-*ass*

sad
triste

treest

happy
heureux/heureuse

er-er/er-erz

nice
bon/bonne

boh/bon

delicious
délicieux/
délicieuse

dayl-eess-yer/dayl-eess-yerz

sweet
sucré/sucrée

syoo-creh/syoo-creh

juicy
juteux/juteuse

shoo-ter/shoot-erz

would you like a.
tu veux un...?

too verz ahn...?

have a...
prends un...

prons ahn

I want a...
je veux un...

sh' verz ahn

A simple guide to pronouncing this French story

Le Singe a perdu sa banane.
ler sanjsh ah pair*doo* sah
ban-*nahn*

Il est triste.
eel eh treest

"Est-ce que tu veux une orange?" dit le Python.
ess ker too verz yoon
o-*ronsh*, dee ler pee*toh*

"C'est bon et juteux."
seh boh eh shoo-*ter*

"Non, merci," dit le Singe.
noh, mair*see*, dee le sanjsh

"Je veux ma banane."
sh' ver mah ban-*nahn*

"Prends quelques noix," dit le Perroquet.
proh *kel*-ker nwah, dee ler
pair-o-*keh*

"Elles sont délicieuses."
el soh dayl-eess-*yerz*

"Non, merci," dit le Singe.
noh mair*see*, dee ler sanjsh

"Je n'aime que les bananes."
sh' nem ker leh ban-*nahn*

"Prends un ananas," dit la Hyène.
prons ahn an-an-*ass*, dee lah ee*yen*

"C'est très sucré."
seh treh syoo*creh*

"Non, merci," dit le Singe.
noh mair*see*, dee ler sanjsh

"Je veux seulement ma banane."
sh' ver serl-*moh* mah ban-*nahn*

"Viens par ici, petit Singe," dit le Tigre.
veeyah par ee-*see*, p'tee sanjsh,
dee ler teegr'

"Je vais te la donner, ta banane."
sh' veh ter lah don-*neh*, tah
ban-*nahn*

Mais le Singe voit sa banane.
meh ler sanjsh vwah sah ban-*nahn*

Et il l'attrape juste à temps!
eh eel lat-*trap* joost ah toh

Le Singe est heureux maintenant.
ler sanjsh et er-*er* mat-*noh*